Be Sensational

AN INSPIRATIONAL TOOLKIT FOR FAMILIES

Be Sensational by Whitney Keyes and Laura T. White

Copyright © 2019 Be Sensational

Illustrations copyright © 2019 by Whitney Keyes
Photographs copyright © 2019 by Danielle Coleman

A Lighthouse Healers Publication
www.besensationalbooks.com
info@besensational.com

Designed by Laura Beers

ISBN: 978-0-578-45133-6

Printed in Canada by Friesens

10 9 8 7 6 5 4 3 2 1

First Edition

Be Sensational

AN INSPIRATIONAL TOOLKIT FOR FAMILIES

WRITTEN BY LAURA T. WHITE
ILLUSTRATED BY WHITNEY KEYES

LIGHTHOUSE HEALERS

If you have one thousand people doing any one yoga pose, what you will have is one thousand variations on the pose. How the pose feels is more important than how the pose looks. If it doesn't feel right, adjust to something that feels better. Close your eyes and find your expression of each pose.

Relax. Breathe. Enjoy.

SENSATIONAL (adj)
  1. of or relating to the senses
  2. exceedingly or unexpectedly excellent or great

Be

Sensational

This is a book about feeling.

Our senses are an exceptional gift. Watching a sunset, biting into a warm chocolate chip cookie, relaxing into the arms of a loved one, smelling a spring rose, listening to a bird singing—we experience life through our senses.

Our senses are something to celebrate.

But sometimes our senses can also be a great challenge, because we live in a flashy, noisy, fast-paced world.

To survive, we tune out the sound of traffic outside our windows. We suffer wearing uncomfortable clothes until we no longer register our skin's discomfort. We learn to live in a lit-up world. By tuning out the uncomfortable experiences, we also lose some of the wonderful sensations. We exist in a "safe" space between the two extremes. If this happens for too long, we feel disconnected from the natural world around us, because in fact we have disconnected from it.

When you get to this place where you are cut off from feeling the world, you are reduced to thinking your way through life. This overloads our brains and leaves us panicked and worried. Our heads aren't meant to do all the work. Your brain works best in partnership with the rest of your body.

Just as your brain is the thinking center of your body, your heart is the feeling center. Returning to our senses and feelings is a return to our hearts. When we live life from our heart, from the center of our being, we are living a sensational life.

Be Sensational was inspired by our years of teaching kids yoga, which encourages children to explore their senses and emotions in a safe and open environment. Children are able to find moments of calm where they can rest in their senses. The more often they do this in class, the more available that calm experience is available to them in their everyday life.

We want to help you get back to a place where you can live life more from the heart. It's a playful, joyful approach to living for you and your family.

Being sensational is something you remember how to be. It's our natural state. The pages in this book are invitations to welcome mindful, sensational living back into your life. Sensational Living is about watching a star-lit sky with awe and gratitude, listening to birds singing, feeling what your body and your emotions are trying to tell you.

You can be an ambassador for the joyful, playful life of being. It's possible. And it's sensational. The first step happens when you invite your senses and emotions to have a place in your life. That's what we've designed these pages to do. You will find ways to celebrate your body and to return to a world in which you can feel again.

Be Sensational offers different ways to explore your senses and feelings as you navigate your sensational body. Only you know how it feels to live in your body, so if the way you experience sight or anger or joy or whatever is different than something we've written, that's great. What's important is how *you* feel. What is most important is that you take the time to feel.

In a desensitized, fast-paced world perhaps the symphony of life only registers as noise. Once you slow down and allow yourself to experience each moment through your senses, the beauty of the music returns.

Mindful living in the present is the secret to survival in our world. To be sensational is to slow down and experience each moment on your terms. When you are able to do this, you experience "being."

This feeling of being might last for a couple of breaths or a couple of moments—don't worry about holding on to it. Once you find it and know it's there, you will be able to return to it again and again.

You can choose to be sensational.

· ·

1

Tuning In with Gratitude

WHAT DO YOU LOVE ABOUT YOURSELF?
WHAT ARE YOU THANKFUL FOR IN YOUR LIFE?

Go on. Make a list.
You can say it, think it, or write the list here on this page.
It can be anything. Don't hold back.
No problem. We'll wait. It's going to be a long list.

I LOVE. . .

WHAT DO YOU LOVE ABOUT YOURSELF?

WHAT ARE YOU THANKFUL FOR?

Keep going. It can be anything.

Do you feel that? When you start to think about the ways you love and are thankful for yourself, you open the door to gratitude.

It begins with you.

Gratitude is the combination of being thankful and feeling loving at the same time. It is the most powerful emotion we have as humans. It can transform everything it touches. Gratitude brings you into the present moment. Tune in to your gratitude and open the door to the joy in your heart.

Gratitude is a feeling we can practice and grow.

Gratitude sets the stage for reconnecting with your sensational body. As you shift your focus from your head down toward your heart and to your body, lining the way with gratitude is like rolling out the red carpet.

Gratitude is what connects us all. It is the feeling that helps us to dissolve the boundaries of you versus me. It is the driving force that connects us to the people and the world around us.

Take a minute each day to give thanks for the things and people in your life for whom you are grateful. Doing this can shift your entire world. It's a sensational way to start (or end . . . or live) each day.

2

Intuition

Many people consider intuition to be the "sixth sense." It's been labeled ESP, or Extra Sensory Perception, and put on a shelf as a special sense, something not present in every person.

Intuition is where it all begins. You are intuitive.

Have you ever had a feeling about someone you just met? You knew you would be friends or you knew they were trouble?

How about feeling you were in a place you shouldn't be? You just knew something bad was about to happen?

Think of a time when you saw an unexpected way out. A solution to a problem you hadn't considered or a feeling of knowing the answer. Maybe you followed a hunch or you denied that feeling and wished you'd gone with your . . . instinct.

Animals have instincts. They can sense a storm coming or know how best to escape a flood. Every elk in the herd "feels" the lion approach, and they know the first one to look up in the direction of the predator will be the big cat's supper.

We are animals too, though sometimes we forget this. Our bodies are wired for intuitive knowing.

You have three main intuition centers in your body.

Your Head – Your brain is constantly thinking and analyzing. Intuition communicates more quietly than the rest of your brain. In the center of your busy brain is a tiny pinecone-shaped gland called the pineal, sometimes referred to as the third eye. The pineal gland doesn't operate like your physical eyes, which see your external surroundings. The third eye views your inner world. This intuition center in the middle of your brain is the wellspring for your dreams and imagination.

Often your intuition will wait until you are deep asleep to talk with you through dreams and visions. Dreams and imagination are your intuition's strongest tools. Allow time to be quiet and still. Soften your gaze or close your eyes to your outside surroundings and open your third eye to the wonderful world within.

Your Heart – Thousands of years ago, a philosopher named Aristotle believed that the heart was the intelligence center of the body. The brain was simply there to cool the wise heart. He might have been onto something. When it comes to emotional intelligence, your heart is the expert.

When you want to know how you really feel about something, ask your heart. It may take some practice to understand the language of your heart, but it's possible. Your heart communicates through pure feeling. The more time you spend listening to your heart and sitting with the feelings living there, the more you will be able to trust in your heart's wisdom. Listen to your heart; it will never steer you wrong.

Your Gut – Gut instinct is real. You experience it in your own unique way, but you have a sensation, a feeling, in your gut when you make a decision. If you consider the best choice, you feel one sensation, while the lesser choice provides another sensation. It may be a twinge, a knot, a sinking sensation, butterfly flutters, or a sense of being settled or calm. Your gut instinct may talk to you through other areas of your body. Goosebumps may rise on your skin when your gut instinct wants to tell you to pay close attention to your surroundings. Your ears may ring when you hear something that your gut doesn't want you to miss.

You have to tune in to your own unique gut language. As you explore your intuition centers, your gut will tell if you are listening to your head or your heart.

Now, let's make friends with your psychic centers. They work best when they are in communication with one another . . .

HEAD • HEART • GUT

Try this:

1. Imagine a tunnel connecting the center of your brain down into the center of your heart.

2. The tunnel has always existed. It might just need some repairs. Notice if the connection to your head is stable and open. Notice the same for the connection to your heart.

3. Use your breath to make sure the tunnel is open, clear and ready to put into use. Feel your breath traveling easily between the two locations.

4. Notice which way energy is traveling once the connection is complete.

5. Take a thought that has been stuck in your brain—something that has been worrying you—and send it down the tunnel into your heart.

6. Once it arrives in your heart, it is no longer a thought. It is a feeling.

7. What is the feeling behind that thought?

8. Ask your heart what to do.

9. Try this exercise with other places in your body. Link your gut to your head, or to your heart.

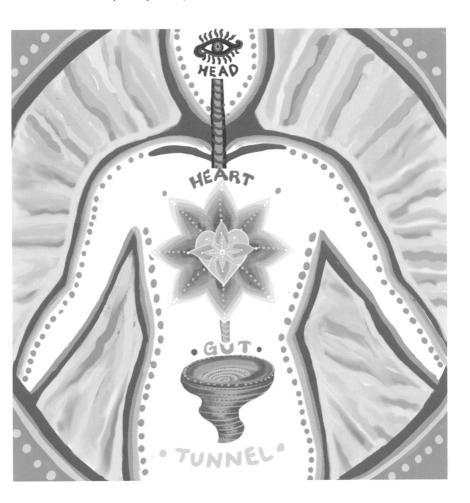

Once these communication channels are operating, you can transform sensory experiences into feelings. You can hear what your intuition channel is trying to tell you.

DREAM VISUALIZATION ·····································

When you sleep, your rational mind gets out of the way for your intuition to play. Your dreamworld provides you with more insight than you might think every night. Just ask questions, and you will see you already know all the answers you seek. Give your dreams space in your waking life and you will be amazed.

1. Before going to sleep, consider what you would like to dream about during the night.

2. Write or draw inspiration for your dream. It might be a question you would like guidance on or a certain place you would like to visit in your dreams.

3. Close your eyes and place your hands over both your physical eyes and your third-eye center. (Palms over the physical eyes and fingers together over the forehead or third-eye center.) The third-eye or mind's eye is located right in between and slightly above the eyebrows. This is where your pineal gland is located.

4. Begin to see your dreams shaping in your imagination.

When you wake in the morning, write or draw about your dreams. What do you remember? It can be anything. "I was scared" or "The color yellow" can be a great start. Dreams work in symbols. A dream about a farm is rarely about an actual farm. It's about what a farm represents.

If you don't remember your dreams at night, you can try this exercise with your daydreams.

MAKE TIME TO DREAM.

· ·

1. Using your toe or a stick, draw a large spiral in the sand. You could use chalk to draw a spiral on blacktop. Spiral around at least three times from your starting point. You have created a circular path.

2. After you create the shape, stand at the outermost entrance on the path. Take a deep breath. Walk slowly to the center.

3. Keep your heart open to receiving any messages or ideas that come your way.

4. Once you reach the center, pause to take a breath or sit quietly for a few minutes. Continue to listen to your heart.

5. When you are ready, make your way back out, following the path.

Draw or journal about how you felt in the labyrinth
or any messages you received here:

CLOUD MESSENGERS ·····························

Have you ever struggled with a problem you just couldn't find the answer to?

Some problems can't be reasoned through. They need a creative solution. That's when you look to the world around you.

The natural world is very connected to our intuition. We receive messages through nature all the time, whether through a certain animal visitor or a weather pattern. Often the answer to our question is as simple as stepping outside and looking to the sky.

1. Ask yourself a question and watch the clouds float by.

2. Allow the shapes of the clouds to play with your imagination.

3. You might see that they remind you of certain animals. You might see faces in the clouds, or really anything. Your imagination is unlimited.

4. Watch as the shapes shift and become new fuel for your imagination.

Are the clouds able to answer your question? Maybe they have another message for you.

Open your eyes to your imagination and open your heart to the possibilities.

See the
magic

TADASANA OR "MOUNTAIN POSE" · · · · · · · · · · · · · · · · · · ·

1. Stand up tall with your feet together.

2. Press down into the earth with your feet.

3. Open both hands, palms facing forward.

4. Reach your arms with strength down by your sides.

5. Stand tall and strong like a mountain. Feel as strong as rock and as heavy as stone. You are a powerful massive mountain reaching up to the sky.

6. What is on your mountain? Are you covered in snow or palm trees? What is the weather?

7. Settle into your own strength. Balance the body front to back and side to side until you can stand super-tall and solid.

Mountain Pose aligns our head, heart, and gut, setting them up for clear communication. When you are out of alignment, one of these three centers might be slightly forward from the others.

When you stand naturally–is one part of your body more forward than the others? That might give you a clue to which area of intuition you rely on the most.

1. Plank Pose is "push-up position" where you are balancing on your hands and your toes. Your stomach is facing the ground.

2. If balancing this way puts too much pressure on your low back, lower your knees to the ground so you are balancing on your hands and knees with your feet supporting.

3. Pull your belly button in so that your low back is neutral. This means there is a natural curve to your back and your abdominal muscles are strong and engaged.

4. Slide your shoulder blades down your back so your neck is long and your ears extend away from your shoulders.

5. Press into the ground so your arms are strong and your chest is proud.

6. Tuck your chin to your chest slightly and pull your head back away from the floor so your neck is long and your head is in line with your shoulders.

Plank Pose is another form of Mountain Pose. Your head, heart, and gut are again in alignment.

· 3 ·

Touch

Skin is the largest organ in the human body. It's a container for our body. We make physical contact with our world through our skin. But you are able to touch people and the world around you without it ever making contact with your skin. The energy that is within and around your body is constantly in contact with your surroundings.

You can physically express love with your skin. A hug from a friend feels good and lights your heart up with joy. Holding somebody's hand or leaning your head on a loved one's shoulder can help you feel connected. Such a simple act, if you slow down to feel it, can bring you into the present moment.

Beyond our skin's sensations, we are also able to feel connections to other people in our lives.

Think of someone you love who needs a little support right now. Close your eyes and tell that person you love them. It doesn't matter if they are a thousand miles away. In that moment, there is a connection between the two of you. Can you feel it?

Now, try the same thing with somebody you know, but not very well. Maybe it's someone you would like to be better friends with. Close your eyes. Send them a smile.

Sometimes we can even feel how we are connected to those we do not know. Compassion is when you are able to feel another's emotional state AND you have a desire to improve it. When you help somebody without expecting a reward or recognition, you are acting compassionately.

Whenever you wonder how to solve a tricky situation, the answer is always to have more compassion. Compassion creates a web of love around us—one that can stretch across the world.

Think of how wonderful it feels to help somebody you love. Remember a time somebody you didn't know at all helped you. You too are able to create a chain reaction of compassion. It can begin in your home, your school, your town . . . but it can reach somebody on the other side of the world whom you've never met.

Imagine our planet encircled by a golden net of compassion, strands of love connecting hearts all around the globe.

You have the power to shift the world around you. All it takes is a smile. It can begin with the touch of your hand.

FEEL YOUR ENERGY

1. Sit in a comfortable position.

2. Bring your hands together in front of your heart, palm to palm as if you were in prayer.

3. Rub your palms together, back and forth, quickly. Keep going. The faster you rub them the more you will be able to feel.

4. Now, separate your hands slowly. Do you feel the buzzing between your hands? You've just woken up your skin's ability to feel the invisible energy vibrating in and around your body.

5. Play with the space between your hands. You can spread it out slowly, like taffy. Ball it up tight. Close your eyes and feel the buzzing sensation as it changes depending on how you move through the energy field.

6. You can try this with friends too. Sit side by side, each creating the friction in your own hands. Then, hold your hands up to your friend's hands a few inches apart. Play with that space between you.

Does the buzzing sensation feel different when you try the exercise with a friend?

Can you feel a shift in the energy based on different words you say? For example, you could say, "I believe in this invisible energy." How does that changes the feeling? You could even say, "I don't believe in this energy." Does that change the way it feels?

WORD TRACING ·

An intention is defined as an aim or purpose. When we focus on a specific intention in our life, we affect our bodies and the world around us.

Scientists have studied the power of intention by watching how water freezes when exposed to particular intentions. Water freezing in the presence of the word "love" froze into beautiful, symmetrical snowflake shapes. Water freezing to the word "hate" became lopsided, misshapen crystals.

Though this energy in and around your body is invisible, you have the power to change the way it feels. You do this through intention. It's a little like magic—whatever you decide to make this energy into, it becomes. Sometimes we do this without thinking. If we think negative thoughts, our energy becomes heavy and uncomfortable. The good news is–you can always change the way your energy feels. You do that by setting intentions. It can be as simple as deciding you want to feel more love. Or joy.

You can try this too:

1. Using a wet paintbrush, paint words on your hands, arms, face, or neck.

2. Choose any word you'd like:
   LOVE   HEALTH   STRENGTH   PATIENCE

3. Remember how powerful your intention is. Be careful what you write because you just might get it.

4. Write your word on paper and tape it to a cup of water.

5. Think of that word for a moment, breathing in its meaning, and focus on the water.

6. Drink the water and imagine filling your body with your intention.

Our bodies are about 65 percent water. Our planet is about 70 percent water. If a single water crystal benefits from feeling love and gratitude, imagine what those intentions would do for our bodies. Imagine what it could mean for our planet.

LOVE COOKIES ·······································

Have you ever wondered what makes Grandma's cookies taste so good?

"They're baked with love," she might say.

It might sound silly, but it's true. We put our emotions into the food we make and when we make food for the people we love, with love, something very special happens.

Let's experience how it feels to bake good intentions into something delicious for someone we love.

1. Find your favorite cookie recipe. Don't have one? I always love the Tollhouse Chocolate Chip Cookie recipe.

2. Wash your hands. Imagine the soapy water catching any negative thought or emotion you might be carrying from your day in its millions of bubbles and washing down the drain. Clean hands, fresh start, full of love.

3. Gather the ingredients.

4. As you combine the ingredients according to the recipe, think of the person you are making the cookies for. (The person doesn't even have to be the one who eats the cookies. Maybe you're baking for a cousin you love who lives far away.) You can remember sweet memories with this person, or fun times you have had together. Maybe the cookies are for you and you can combine the ingredients while you think about the list of things you love about yourself from page 15.

5. Enjoy balling the sticky dough into spoonful drops on the cookie sheet. With each cookie you put down, imagine you are coating the dough with gratitude.

6. Bake the cookies.

7. Once they cool, share them with that special somebody. Share them with everybody. Enjoy them for yourself too.

PASCHIMOTTANASANA OR "SEATED FORWARD FOLD"

Forward folds are an excellent way to tune in to and calm your body. The lean in makes us listen to our heart's beat or follow the waves of our breath.

1. Sit with feet hip width apart.

2. Bend your knees until you can rest your chest and heart on your thighs.

3. Rest your forearms on your shins, one on top of the other.

4. Relax your forehead on your forearms.

5. Tilt the entire bowl of your hips forward, as though you were pouring out the contents. (Make sure to bend at the crease of the hips and not the bottom of the spine.)

Important note: It does not matter how far you have to bend your knees, let your heart rest on your thighs. You can prop pillows below your bent knees so you can really relax. Only straighten your knees as far as your lower back feels comfortable.

UTTANASANA OR "STANDING FORWARD FOLD" · · · · ·

1. Stand with feet hip distance apart.
2. Reach your arms to the sky to stretch your spine as long as you can.
3. Swan dive your chest and heart forward, keeping the spine as long as you can.
4. Bring your heart to your thighs. Bend the knees as much as you need to get your chest in contact with your thighs.
5. Release your spine. Let gravity stretch you long and loose.
6. Shake your head yes and no to release any tension in your neck. Pour over your legs to the earth.

· · · · · · · · · · · · ·  · · · · · · · · · · · · ·

ANJALI MUDRA OR "HANDS IN PRAYER"

1. Bring your palms together in front of your heart.

It is simple to practice and very powerful.

In India, this gesture is also used to give thanks, to express gratitude.

Return to your truth and your heart.

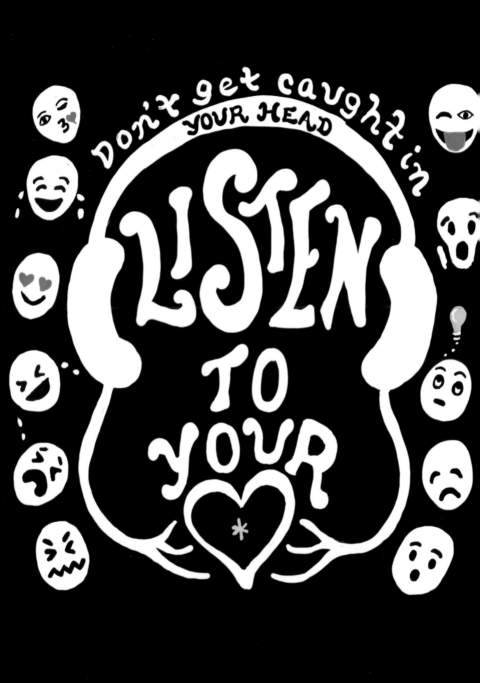

Sound

LISTEN CLOSELY.

Hearing and listening are two very different things. We can hear with our ears, but we listen with our hearts. When the two work in concert, we are sure to find the truth.

When we are afraid, our hearing goes into hyperalert mode. When our intuition or one of our other senses cues in to danger, we stop and really listen. Emergency alert systems know this about our bodies, so detected danger is often accompanied by alarms or sirens.

When we are scared, we might want to close our eyes or hide or run from the danger, but we won't stop listening and gauging how close the danger might be or where we need to go to avoid it.

Our bodies aren't meant to be afraid for long periods of time. In the animal kingdom, after a herd animal is chased down by a predator and escapes, it doesn't hang on to that fearful memory. It shakes the fear from its system and goes back to living life, only calling on fear when it helps it to run.

Our world is fast, busy, and loud. Sometimes these sensory experiences can convince us that we are in danger when we are not. Let your ears communicate with your heart so you can know when to run, when to stand your ground, and when to let yourself feel peace.

How do we transform fear? With courage and love.

Courage is not the absence of fear. When you are afraid, yet choose to focus on strength to move through fear, then you are being courageous. It's like climbing a high dive, walking to the end of the wobbly board, looking down, and choosing to jump even though you are afraid. Courage brings us to the point where we break through fear to splash into our joy.

YOU ARE COURAGEOUS.

Listen to your intuition. It will remind you of this again and again.

SOUND TRAVELS

You'll need a bell, signing bowls, triangles, metal mixing bowls or any other percussion instrument that creates a vibrational sound that slowly fades.

1. Sit and take a moment to be quiet.

2. Close your eyes and have a partner play a sound on the instrument you are using.

3. Keeping your eyes closed, use your concentration to follow the sound.

4. Use your body to FEEL the sound.

5. Use your awareness to hear the sound spread through the room until it finally disappears.

6. Sit with that silence. Imagine the wave of the sound spreading out to the world around you, all the way across and out as far as you can imagine.

Take a moment to draw or write about how listening to sound spread without using your sight makes you feel.

INSIDE VS. OUTSIDE NOISES ···························

1. Listen with your eyes closed to noises inside the room.
2. What do you hear?
3. Keeping your eyes closed, can you judge where the things are that are making sounds?
4. Now, take a moment to try to focus on noises outside the room.
5. How far away are these sounds?
6. Which are easier to focus on, the near sounds or the faraway ones? *(If you are in nature you can focus on near and faraway noises.)*
7. Cover your ears and close your eyes and listen to the sound of your breath.
8. What does your breathing sound like?
9. Can you also hear your heart beating? Try holding your hands over your heart. Does that help you to listen?
10. Cover your ears with your hands. Listen to your breathing. Listen to the beating of your heart.
11. Slow your breathing to match the beat of your heart. Try three beats to breathe in and three to breathe out.
12. Experiment with different numbers of heartbeats per breath.

BEYOND FEAR

We all have wonderful gifts to share with the world.

Wonder what yours are?

Ask yourself the following:

If I were not afraid, I would _____.

Or, I'd be _____.

Without fear, I feel _____.

Take whatever that blank is, and use all your courage to work through your fear. You are stacked with courage. You just have to see your fear and know what's beyond it.

YOU are beyond your fear.

SHAKE IT OFF ··

Has anybody ever told you to shake something off? Did you know that shaking your body can help you change your mood? Shaking gets us out of our heads and back into our hearts. Just as you would shake up a bottle of salad dressing before using it because the ingredients work best when blended, the same idea works for your body. Shaking gets your whole body refreshed and working together. When your body feels fresh, your brain works better too.

WHEN YOU GET STUCK IN FEAR, ·
TRYING SHAKING THE GRIP OF FEAR LOOSE.

1. Put on your favorite dance song.

2. Shake your right hand to the music. Let the shake work its way up your right arm. Shake for twenty seconds or so.

3. Now, shake your left hand, working into the left arm.

4. Shake your left leg, balancing on your right.

5. Now your right leg.

6. Lay on your back and shake both legs up to the ceiling.

7. Shake your shoulders.

8. Shake your belly.

9. Shake your hips as fast as you can.

10. Shake your whole body.

11. Repeat as necessary.

12. When you are done shaking, stand still, close your eyes and feel the fresh buzzing sensation in your body.

13. Feel the beating of your heart. It is probably pumping very quickly. You might place a hand over the beating in your chest, find a comfortable seat, close your eyes and sit with your heart as it slows back to a normal pace.

14. Breathe deeply. Are there any messages from your heart now that it isn't gripped with the stuck emotion? Listen to—*feel*—your heartbeat for as long as you can.

BALASANA OR "CHILD'S POSE" ·

1. Kneeling with your shins on the ground, shift your hips back onto your heels. If this is uncomfortable on your knees or ankles, grab a pillow and place it under your bum between your feet to lift your hips higher. That should take the pressure off your joints.

2. Rest your heart down onto your thighs.

3. Stretch your arms out in front of you so that your palms rest on the ground.
   * Or, you can bring your arms back by your sides, with the palms of your hands facing up and your thumbs by the edge of your feet.
   * Or, you can make a pillow for your head with your hands. Reach your arms forward, bend at the elbows bringing hands together into a triangle shape under your forehead.

4. Rest your head.

5. Try all three arm positions and choose which one feels more relaxing.

6. Imagine that you are a seed, soaking in all you will need to grow into a beautiful tree.

7. Feel the sun on your back. Let your breath be the fuel you need to grow.

CHANT "OM" ······························

Om is the sacred sound of the universe, according to Hindu texts. Chanting "Om" connects you to the universe. While chanting this word it is as if your physical body fades away and the light within you connects with the supreme light of the world.

Om consists of three syllables: ah, oh and mmmm.
Try chanting Om now.

1. Take a deep breath in, and release.
2. Now inhale for Om.
3. *Ahhhhhhh, oooooooohhhhhhhhh. Mmmmmmmmm.*
4. Again.
5. Again.
6. After the third Om, rest in the silence.
7. Breathe deeply, breathing in the silent space around you.
8. Notice as your everyday sounds and noises begin to fill the space again.

DIGEST YOUR

TASTE YOUR GUT INSTINCT

EMOTIONS

· 5 ·

Taste

Have you ever been so hungry or in such a hurry that you didn't taste a single bite?

We train our bodies from a young age to desire certain tastes, but food stimulates more than our sense of taste. We may try a new food because its scent pleases us. We may stay away from another food because its texture repels us. Seeing a bright red strawberry is more appealing than a pale one. By the time we taste a food, we have already had an entire sensational relationship with it.

Is it possible to experience taste alone?

Our bodies are constantly "digesting" the world around us. This includes processing our sensory experiences and our emotions. Add to that all the food you eat, and our digestive systems are very busy indeed.

When you slow down all that you are taking in— meaning when you really chew and taste your food—you give taste a chance to enrich your life.

Remember that you are intuitive. One of your body's intuition centers resides in your gut. Taste is the gateway to your gut. Taking time to taste life allows your intuition an opportunity to share its wisdom with you.

Your gut can also tell you when you are on the right track, like a guide. It might grumble when you experience truth or ache when you are making the wrong choice. Your stomach will always tell you what is right and what is wrong if you are willing to listen to its messages.

Nothing confuses your gut instinct like worry. Have you experienced the wringing sensation of worry in your stomach? Trying to hear intuitive messages from a stomach twisted with worry is like trying to read the words written on a crumpled piece of paper.

When your worry releases, you are able to digest your food better, but there is something more—you free up your intuition center in your gut so it can communicate more clearly.

TONGUE MAP

Your tongue map is a virtual wonderland of taste experiences.

Each flavor is categorized in your mouth. Sometimes the flavor is quick to make itself known. Sometimes it can take a while and you are left with an aftertaste.

You experience these tastes in so many ways, throughout your mouth and digestive tract.

Try this:

1. Gather a bunch of different foods. You will need something:
   SWEET   SALTY   SOUR   SPICY
2. Bite into each food.
3. Where do you first experience the taste of the food?
4. Does the experience change? Sweet to sour, etc?
5. Does the taste move?
6. Does the taste change when you chew it? Does chewing lessen or intensify the taste?
7. What happens when you swallow?
8. Is there an aftertaste?

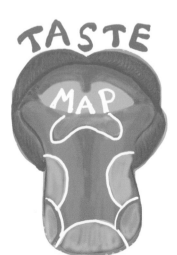

Try this with each of the foods you've gathered. Map the experiences on the tongue map at the left.

BLINDFOLD TASTING

1.
With a friend, gather
a collection of tasty foods.

2.
One person is blindfolded, and the other carefully
feeds their blindfolded friend samples of the food.

3.
Go slowly.

4.
Allow plenty of time to chew and taste each bite.

5.
Without your sight, does your food taste different?

6.
What happens if you say "blueberry" but give a strawberry instead?

7.
Try different flavors of food—sweet, salty, savory, or sour.

8.
Does something sweet taste sweeter after something sour?

9.
After trying this for a while, remove the blindfold and take a
few bites of everything so you can see what you're tasting.

10.
Is the experience different?

After you end the exercise switch places and
become the feeder or the receiver. Sit still for
a moment after you are done and focus on
how it makes your heart feel.

♥

don't
peek

GUT BOWL – Everything but the Kitchen Sink

Our body tries to keep us safe by sending us messages from our intuition. One of the fastest ways to get our attention is through our gut. Messages from our stomach or gut are called "gut instinct."

To experience your gut instinct:

1. Get a large bowl from your kitchen.
2. Go through your cabinets, your refrigerator, your spice cabinet and gather any ingredient that catches your attention. Suggestions include:

Ketchup	Lemons
Salt	Spinach
Cinnamon	Butter
Milk	Yogurt
Pickles	Cottage cheese
Orange juice	

3. Think of gross ingredients—seriously, anything works as long as it is edible. The more disgusting the combination the better.
4. Now, mix it all into the bowl. Mix it well.
5. Scoop up a spoonful. Hold it to your mouth. Smell it. You are about to take a bite.
6. How does your stomach feel? Does it want you to eat this disgusting slop? That's your gut instinct sending you a message.

WILL YOU LISTEN TO YOUR GUT? OR

WILL YOU TAKE A BIG HEAPING SPOONFUL?

HOW DOES IT FEEL TO TUNE IN TO YOUR GUT?

Worry can feel like a tightening in your belly. This leads to tightness in other places in your body. You might hold stress and worry in your neck and shoulders. Maybe your back is stiff and rigid or your hands or legs clench even when you are sitting and "relaxed."

You can tell your body to relax, but often there are layers of tension built up over time. You can't think your way to a less tense body. You have to melt the tension a layer at a time.

TRY THIS:

1. Lie down and take three deep breaths in and out.

2. Ball your hands into tight fists. Hold the fists until your hands are shaking. Maybe the shake even works its way up your arms. Your shoulders might eventually shake from the squeezing.

3. Take a deep breath in.

4. Exhale and release the fists. Imagine you are breathing out all the tension in your hands.

5. Try the same thing with your feet. Flex your feet back or scrunch your feet like a monkey trying to hold onto a branch with his feet.

6. Hold the tightness in your feet until the shake starts to work its way up your legs.

7. Take a deep breath in.

8. Exhale, and release all the tension in your feet. Just breathe it out.

9. Now, scrunch every muscle in your face. Pinch your mouth and squeeze your eyes shut. Wrinkle your nose and even imagine your ears are being tightened by the tension in your jaw as your teeth clench. Everything is tight and wrinkled and squished.

10. Deep breath in.

11. Breathe it out. And release.

12. Try the same thing with your belly. Crunch your belly so that your shoulders and even your hips lift up off the ground. Pull your arms and your legs into your body. Squeeze, squeeze, squeeze.

13. Deep breath in.

14. Breathe it out. And release.

15. Try your entire body. Every muscle is tense. Hold it, hold it, hold it, and feel the tension shaking through your body.

16. Deep breath in.

17. Breathe it out and release.

18. Do a couple rounds of the full body tensing and releasing.

19. Relax flat on your back. Really let the floor hold you up. Take ten more breaths. Each breath is sweeping your body for remaining tension. Breathe in to collect any tension. Breathe out to let it escape from your body. Rest in that soft space for as long as you are able.

ARDHA MATSYENDRASANA OR "SEATED TWIST"

1. Begin sitting with both legs extended in front of you.

2. Cross your right leg over the left, bringing your right foot to the ground on the outside of your left leg.

3. Now, lean to your left. Your right hip will rise off the ground.

4. Bend your left leg to bring your heel by your bum. If it hurts the left leg to bend it that deeply, you can keep the bottom leg straight because the important part is the twist. You are a human pretzel in this pose.

5. Reach both arms up high to the sky. Sit taller than you have all day long.

6. Twist your body toward the top bent knee with your belly button facing your upper leg. Hug your bent knee. *Twisssssst.*

7. If you want to twist further, then bring your right elbow to the outside of your right knee and press into it to spin you right round. Imagine your body is a wet towel and you are wringing out the towel to squeeze out all the water.

8. Stay here for a couple of breaths.

9. Release the twist

10. Uncross you legs, and then repeat on the opposite side, with your left leg crossed up and over the right.

SIMHASANA OR "LION'S BREATH"

1. Close your eyes.

2. Take a deep breath in.

3. Exhale and let your tongue extend out like a lion yawning.

4. Exhale. Make sound as you force the air out. *Haaaaaaaa!* Make that *haaaaaaaa* as loud as possible.

5. Imagine you are clearing the body of anything it no longer needs.

LOOK AT THE BIG PICTURE

·6·

Sight

Can you open your mind big enough to see the whole picture?

The eyes help us see. Our mind helps us understand what we are seeing. Our heart helps us know if we are seeing things from the right point of view. Our gut tells us how to respond to what we are seeing.

Sight is a wonderful way to see the world exactly as it is right now, but sometimes strong emotions can effect our perspective. Anger, for instance, can shift our vision. When we are angry, we see things people are doing as intentional or spiteful. Anger makes our view very narrow.

Some people literally "see red" when they get angry. That makes sense because anger feels a little like hot lava bubbling up from deep in the belly. By the time the lava reaches the top of the volcano, everybody had better look out.

If you are seeing red, it's time to listen to that anger, let it tell you its message, and then you can begin to refocus on the world around you to see the whole picture or to determine how you can put that anger into positive action. The only way to rise above

WHEN
ANGER
BOILS OVER

anger is perspective. You need to get an eagle's-eye view of the situation.

If you see somebody treating another person unfairly, take a moment to "see" the whole situation, and then see how you can get involved to help ease the situation. Your vision can help you problem-solve, to become a peacemaker in the world around you. Every little bit helps. You can bring peace into any situation one breath at a time.

It takes courage to look at a situation from a different point of view. Once you see the bigger picture, you can have compassion for others involved. Compassion is when you can see from someone else's point of view, but it's more than that. With compassion you can feel their hurt feelings and also want to help them feel better. Compassion enables you to start creating solutions to problems that once only made you angry. Bridges of compassion help to break up anger.

FIND YOUR COURAGE. Build bridges of compassion and watch anger melt into love and joy. See the whole picture.

BLIND BALANCE ······································

Your eyes help your body know where it is in relationship to other things. This is called proprioception. A lot of our special understanding comes from our sight. When you alter that, you confuse your body awareness.

The more you practice with altered states of vision, the better your body sense will become.

"Drishti" is a term used in yoga to describe a specific gaze in a pose. When you focus your gaze, or drishti, you can limit distractions in the room/world around you. Drishti is very important in balancing poses. If your eyes are focused on something that is unmoving and constant, your brain and body are better able to stay balanced.

To see how powerful this tool can be, first try balancing without a set gaze:

1. Begin standing balanced on two feet.
2. Pour all your weight into one leg and lift the other leg so that you are balancing on one leg.
3. Once you have your balance, close one eye for a couple of breaths.
4. Next, switch which eye you have closed.
5. Open both eyes for a few breaths and try balancing on one leg with both eyes closed.
6. You might also try turning your head to look over one shoulder and then the next. Both eyes are open but you might notice a change in your balance as your eyes sweep from side to side.
7. Now, steady your gaze. Look at something in the distance that is still and steady. Breathe deeply. How does this affect your balance?
8. Try all these options while balancing on the other leg.

Do you notice a difference between sides?
Does it get easier or more difficult if you try both sides again?
What if you look up and down while balancing?
Experiment with another focal point. You might even try watching something that is moving in the distance.

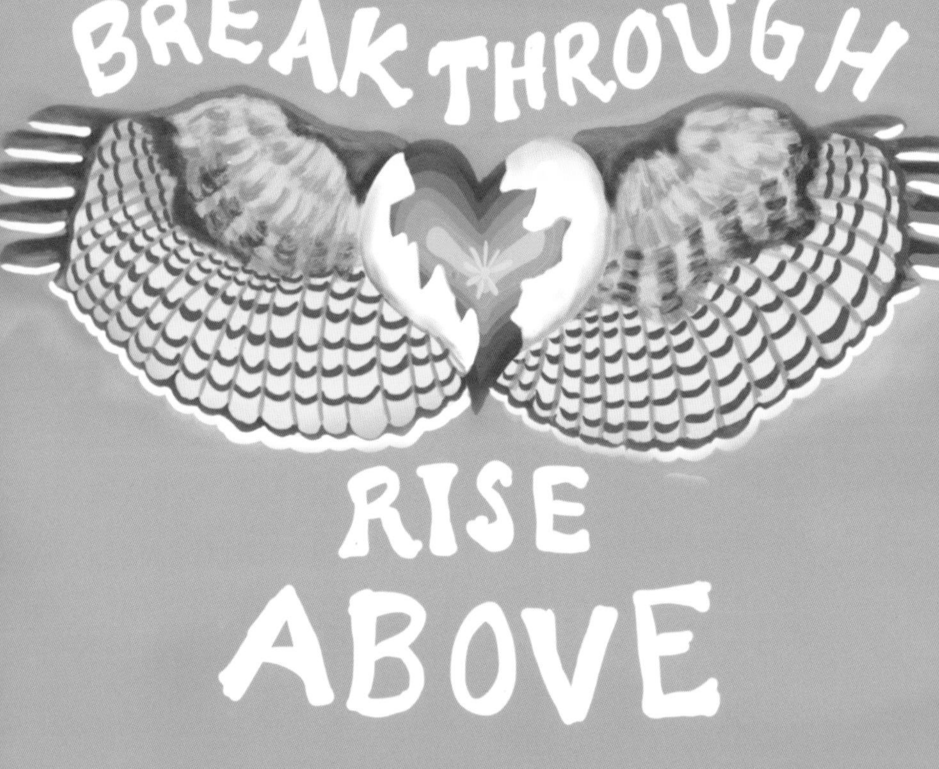
BREAK THROUGH
RISE
ABOVE

See it for what it is.

Our eyes work like cameras, sending images to our brains.

The trick is to see the picture of the world around us without bringing a story or a memory to the present moment.

1. Close your eyes. Face forward.
2. Open your eyes. See what's in front of you. Just as you feel a thought, or story, start to form in your brain based on what you see, close your eyes and turn your head.
3. Think of the image you just saw as a single snapshot or photograph.
4. Your eyes are closed, facing the right.
5. Open your eyes. See what's in front of you. Just as you feel a thought start to form in your brain based on what you see, close your eyes and turn your head.
6. You've just taken another "photograph" with your eyesight.
7. Repeat, looking to the left.
8. Then look up.
9. Then again, looking down.
10. Facing forward again, eyes closed, let all those memories of what's around you exist as pure photos, free from thought or attached memories.

ROAR

Imagine you are the angry tiger who has lived too long in a cage. Roar deep and wild, until your keeper has no choice but to unlock the gate and set you free. You can pace the room like a tiger. You might find you've created the cage. Your body is the cage for your anger and you've held the key the entire time.

SCREAM

This is great to do in the car with the windows rolled up. The entire family can scream together. Driving down a highway, you can blast the radio and scream at the top of your lungs. You might even end up laughing. Remember, emotions often exist in layers. Your anger might be keeping you from being in direct contact with your sadness, hurt, or joy. Open yourself to what is underneath.

BREAK

Buy at least a dozen eggs per person. Find a place outside like your own backyard. Hold an egg, put whatever emotion you are struggling with into that egg, wind up, and give it a good throw. Once your egg cracks and splatters, your emotion will begin to transform. It might take a dozen eggs, or it might take three dozen, but you'll set the tiger free.

Watch your anger disperse and spread out.

What was beneath your anger? How do you feel now?

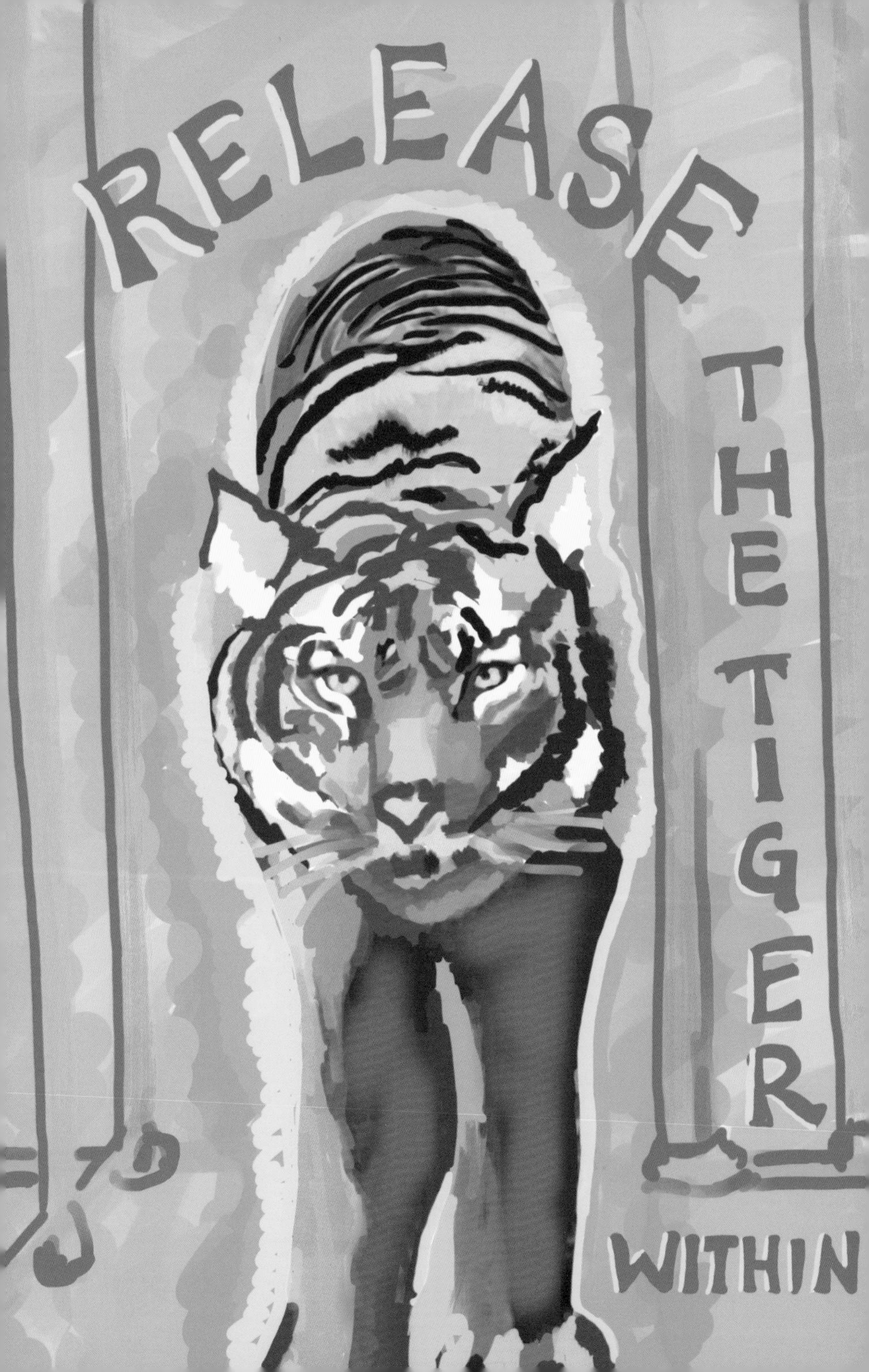
RELEASE
THE TIGER
WITHIN

THROWING ROCKS ·

Whatever the reason for your anger, the first step in learning from the experience of getting mad is to sit and actively FEEL your feeling.

Anger is a protective instinct. We do not want to deny or squash it. At the same time, we do not want to fuel it or stew in it either. Holding on to anger only hurts us more. We tend to get angry when we get hurt. We get angry to try to stop FEELING the hurt.

Anger shows us when we need to say no or draw a boundary. *No, don't talk to me like. No, don't treat me like that.* Once you have gotten mad and drawn a boundary line, only then can you thank your protective instinct and release the hurt that caused you to get angry in the first place.

1. Go to a body of water, whether it is a lake, pond, or quiet river.
2. Find some rocks in the surrounding area. The heavier the better, especially for the things that have made you really angry.
3. Pick up the rocks. Whisper to them what you are mad about or the words that were said that hurt you. Thank the anger for what it has taught you.
4. Throw that rock as hard you can into the water.

Write or draw about how your heart felt doing this exercise.

5. Watch the splash as the rock makes contact with the water's surface. After that first big splash, circular ripples will spread out over the surface of the water, wider and wider until they disappear. See your anger spread out and disappear.

6. Get as many rocks as you need. You might have a lot of things you are mad about. One at a time, address the reason for your anger. Thank it, and then throw each rock as hard you can.

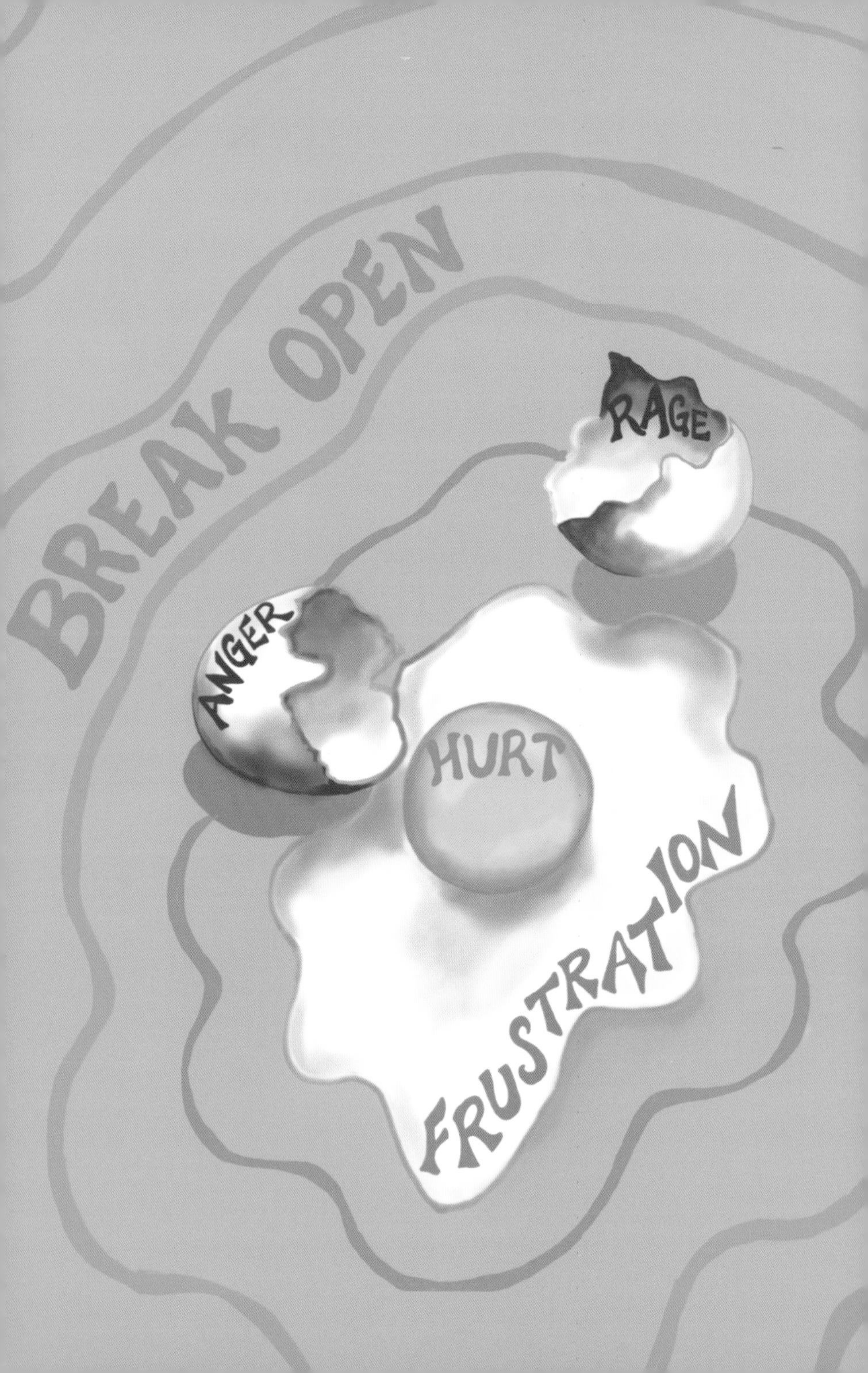
BREAK OPEN
RAGE
ANGER
HURT
FRUSTRATION

ANGER MANDALA

Anger is only the hard shell. Break it open.
Identify what deep hurt is at the center.

No matter how hard we try to make ourselves,
the beauty is in breaking open and revealing
the contents inside.

Decorate the mandala to express or describe
what you found beneath the shell of your anger.

GARUDASANA OR "EAGLE POSE"

Eagles have excellent vision and are able to see their prey from two miles away. Channel the sight of an eagle with this powerhouse of a pose.

1. Stand on one foot.
2. Lift the opposite leg and wrap it around the other. Only go as far as is comfortable for your knees. You can even use the toe of your wrapped leg as a kickstand for balance.
3. Bend your knees.
4. Gather your power.
5. Use your eagle's eye to find your balance.
6. Place your palms together. Find your center.
7. Bend your knees deeper, hug your elbows in, and imagine you are an eagle crouched to leap into flight, watching your prey far in the distance.
8. Uncrossing your legs, jump up and spread your arms, leaping into flight. *Kaaaa!*

VIPARITA KARANI OR "LEGS UP THE WALL" ·················

1. Sit on the floor with one hip against the wall and legs along the edge of where the wall and floor meet.
2. Keeping your bum against the wall, lean away from it to lower your upper body to the ground.
3. If your bum loses contact with the wall, shimmy it closer.
4. Roll onto your back, so your legs are resting on the wall with your bum as close to the wall as possible.
5. Lie flat on your back and breathe. If you feel any pain in your back you can always put a pillow under your bum or shimmy a little away from the wall and bend your knees. The blood will slowly begin to drain from your toes (they might tingle—that's okay) to soak in your heart.
6. See if you can feel the blood refreshing all the organs in your belly.

This is a wonderful pose to do before bedtime, as it revitalizes your organs and relaxes the nervous system. Hold this pose for five minutes.

·7·

Smell

Your sense of smell is closely related to your memory bank. How does your favorite holiday smell?

How about your favorite season?

What about your best friend's house?

Or your school?

Smells link our past to our present. They can feel a lot like a time machine, bringing you back to your first day of school or a vacation you took years ago.

But how often do you take the time to really breathe in your surroundings?

Do you stop to smell the roses?

Now is your chance.

Smell is also a powerful way to change your mood. If you are worried, smell the flower beside you. It will help to stop the worry spiral. If you are angry, breathe deeply, drawing in the scent of the room around you. You can shift your mood by breathing in different ways. Breathing intentionally draws you back to the present.

Sadness can be a heavy emotion. Think of the heaviness in your chest when you are sad. Feeling sadness when it comes to call is a way to turbocharge the joy in your life. It acts like a springboard—the deeper you feel into the truth of your sadness, the more you open yourself up to its contrast.

Sadness is like a storm cloud covering the light and joy in your heart. Just like the sun in a storm, the joy is still there.

Remember a time you cried so hard you had no tears left? If you can find the laughter on the other side of those tears, you've found a secret passageway between emotions. Living life in the "safety" above the pain of sadness also limits how high you can climb into your joy. Unlock the depths of your emotions and there is no limit to how high you can soar.

Breathing in the beauty of life is the remedy for sadness. It's how you transform sadness. Breathe deeply and access sweet, kind, loving memories through your sense of smell.

BOUQUETS OF BOUQUETS ··································

Pick a bouquet of flowers for someone you love.

1. You might pick your flowers in a garden, a field, or in a florist shop.

2. Smell each flower you see.

3. Which flowers smell best?

4. Does the scent match the color in your expectation?

5. Does size make a difference in scent? Do big flowers have a stronger smell?

6. Collect a bouquet or an arrangement of flowers and give them to somebody you love. Maybe that somebody is you.

What's for dinner tonight?

1. Find your favorite dinner recipe.
2. Collect all the ingredients.
3. One by one, add the ingredients together according to the recipe.
4. Take a moment to smell each ingredient before adding it to the recipe.
5. After each ingredient, smell the whole mixture again. Notice the changes.
6. Once the ingredients are baking together, notice when you can start to smell them as the dish you remember eating.
7. How far does the scent travel while it is cooking? To the next room?
8. Step outside for a minute and then come back in. Is the smell stronger?
9. Once the meal is ready, sit and enjoy it with your family.

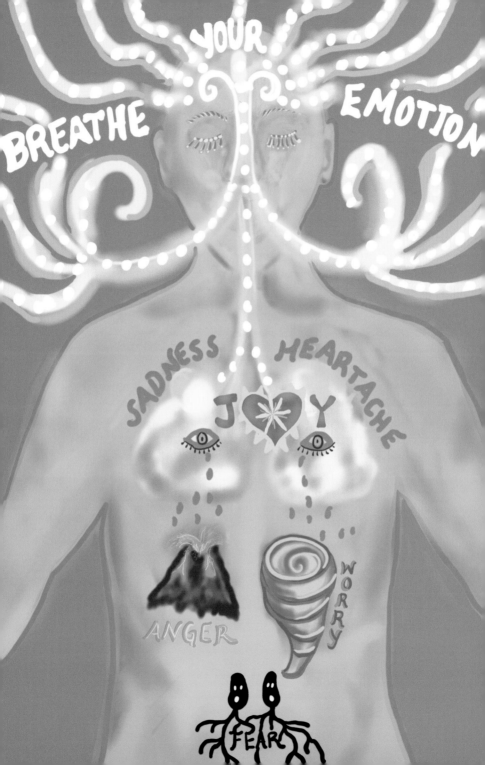

BREATHING YOUR EMOTIONS ·······················

Your feelings are energy in motion inside your body.

This is why feelings are also called emotions.

E = energy

Motion = moving inside of you

Sensing and allowing your emotions to speak to your heart is a very important part of being sensational.

Sometimes your feelings are welcome, like being full of excitement, wonder, or love. Other times feelings are uncomfortable, like being caught in fear, exploding in anger, or weighted down by sadness.

Whatever it is you are feeling, it is key to allow these messages to occur because the only way to get back to your natural state of joy is by first being able to sit with that uncomfortable emotion. If you can sit and really know what your emotions are trying to tell you instead of bottling them inside, then you can find your way back to joy, which is always in the center of your heart.

Remember the last time you cried until you couldn't breathe?

How about a time when you laughed so hard your cheeks hurt?

Every emotion comes with its own unique breath.

When we are calm, we might sigh. When we are angry, we might grunt and snort. Just as our emotions cause us to breathe a certain way the reverse is also true. Our breath can cause us to feel certain emotions.

TRY THIS:

1. Laugh. Even if it isn't real—pretend somebody just told you the funniest joke of your life.

2. Laugh and let it shake your body. Hold your belly and feel it jiggle with laughter. Keep it up for a minute.

   HOW DO YOU FEEL?

3. Now, breathe in and out very quickly. Keep your breath just in your chest—short, shallow, rapid breaths. Keep it going for up to a minute.

   HOW DO YOU FEEL?

4. Take a deep breath in through your nose and let it out in a long, satisfying sigh. Try breathing in and sighing for an entire minute, maybe ten to fifteen breaths.

   HOW DO YOU FEEL?

How do you breathe when you feel other emotions? Create your own exercises for all your feelings. Which emotions are you able to experience most easily through changing your breath? Which do you feel works the fastest? Are there any emotions you have trouble feeling through this method? Why do you think that is?

DECORATING WITH TEARS ················

Sometimes the best medicine really is a good cry.

Crying is how our bodies rebalance, naturally. Making tears creates a chemical reaction in the body.

It's important to shed tears, so each of us needs to find a safe place to cry. The next time you feel overwhelmed and those tears start to build up behind your eyes:

1. Find a quiet space where you can be alone or with a favorite supporter and let those tears fall.

2. You can sob, make noise, wail if you have to. Just don't hold back.

3. Choose to be in your emotion without being embarrassed about it.

4. Imagine that each tear is a beautiful crystal diamond. As they streak down your cheeks, they make pathways of light on your skin. As they splash to the floor each tear spreads out into a stitch on an exquisite carpet around you.

5. Catch your tears and hang them like paintings on the walls around you.

6. Use your imagination to decorate a sacred space with your tears and see how that intention transforms each tear from something that must be hidden into something beautiful you are secretly sharing with the world.

Early yogis named their poses after things they saw in nature. Plants (Lotus Pose), animals (Crow Pose) and geography (Mountain Pose) all inspired traditional yoga poses. The "Dog Poses" imitate how a dog stretches, first reaching his tail to the sky, then lifting his chest with his nose to the sky.

A dog's sense of smell is 10,000 to 100,000 times as strong as that of a human. In these poses, imagine what that would be like. With a dog's nose you could smell scents that had been left behind a very long time ago. You could detect a scented message from a friend even if it had been covered by another person's message. How would you use a super-sensitive nose?

ADHO MUKHA SVANASANA OR "DOWNWARD-FACING DOG" ····················

1. Begin in Plank Pose (p. 32), which is the top of a push-up. Spread your fingers wide right under your shoulders.

2. Keeping your arms and legs strong and straight, press into your hands and lift your "tail" to the sky. Your back stays in one long line from your tail to the top of your head.

3. Look to your belly (which is pulled tight) or to your thighs. Let your neck be long, with your shoulders pulled away from your ears.

4. You might bend your knees to lift your tail higher to the sky. Wag your tail. Maybe straighten one leg and then the other as you try to press your heels toward the ground.

5. Try straightening both legs, but only if it feels good. The goal is to have a long, straight spine.

URDHVA MUKHA SVANASANA OR "UPWARD-FACING DOG"

1. From Downward-Facing Dog, come back to Plank Pose (top of a push-up).

2. Lower your belly to the ground. Your hands are still wide on the mat below your shoulders with your elbows bent up alongside your body.

3. Leading with your nose, scoop your head and chest forward and up toward the sky. This is a backbend. Your hips are low to the ground, your chest is proud and open with a long neck because your shoulders are reaching away from your ears. Your face is slightly lifted to the sky.

4. Untuck your toes so that the tops of your feet are on the mat and your toes point to the wall behind you. If it is okay with your low back, press into your hands and try to lift your thighs off the mat so that you are balancing between your hands and the tops of your feet.

5. Breathe in the world around you.

NADI SHODHANA PRANAYAMA OR "ALTERNATE NOSTRIL BREATHING"

Breathing through one nostril and then the other brings your mind, body, and mood into balance. Try this to calm yourself or to recenter and connect with your heart when your head is too busy.

1. Find a comfortable seat.

2. With your right hand, lower your pointer and middle finger down. You will use your right ring finger and pinkie to open/close your left nostril and your right thumb to close your right nostril.

3. Take a few deep breaths in and out through your nose.

4. Close your right nostril and breathe in through your left nostril.

5. At the top of the breath, switch sides, closing your left nostril and opening your right nostril.

6. Exhale through your right nostril.

7. Breathe in through your right nostril.

8. Switch sides again.

9. Breathe out through your left nostril.

10. Breathe in through your left nostril.

11. Switch sides and breathe out through your right nostril.

Continue breathing in one side and out the other, alternating for a couple minutes.

Joy

Joy is our body's natural state. So many people live their life in search of joy, wondering when it will come into their lives. The truth is—we are each already unlimited wells of joy. We have a never-ending supply of joy inside us. The well of joy in our bodies is inside our hearts.

Once we move down out of our busy heads and live life from the heart in balance with our head and the rest of our body, we are able to experience the joy we've been carrying around with us all the while.

You know that moment when you've laughed until your belly hurts and you draw in that deep sigh of a breath? Right there you are shining joy from your heart. You are in direct contact with that feeling. But laughter is an easy bridge to joy.

Joy is also waiting for you at the very end of a good long cry. It's that ragged breath you draw into your shaking lungs when the tears stop.

It's the buzzing feeling you have when you've shaken worry from your body. It's the release you

feel when the egg of anger breaks wide open and you are free from its hold.

Joy is waiting for you to step out of the past and forget about the future for a moment and just BE. Right here. Right now. It might be one sweet breath away. It could be the taste of your favorite treat. It could be riding the sound waves of your favorite song. Once you stop and give it time to make itself known to you, you will realize it's been there all along.

Joy is beneath, above, and around every experience of your life. When you are able to let the feelings rise up and through you, when you make friends with your emotions, then you will find that life is lived in a river of joy. We exist "in joy."

EN-JOY LIFE.

Mindful (adj.) – to become conscious or aware of something

Mindfulness is more than a buzzword. It's a modern-day goal. To live mindfully . . . that is the great challenge of our age.

We use our senses and listen to our emotions to increase our awareness of the world around us and the world inside our bodies. The funny thing is–these sensory experiences and big emotions can send so much information to our brains–that it sometimes does feel like we are filling our brains to the point of bursting.

Mind-Full? Aren't our heads already full and racing?

Maybe it's time to be Heart-Full.

Filling your head can make it feel busy, but filling your heart brings you more and more joy, because that is the natural state of your heart.

Your heart is open to suggestion. Very open, in fact. If you think of what you want more of in your life and in your heart, your heart will help you to find what it is you seek. Be careful what you ask for. You just might get it.

What do you want
your heart to be filled with?

BE:

PLAYFUL

HEALTHFUL

HEARTFUL

JOYFUL

INSIGHTFUL

SOULFUL

BEACILFUL

ADD YOUR IDEAS TO THIS LIST.

Write or draw them here.

HEART WALL VISUALIZATION ···································

Living with an "open heart," one where feelings and information travel freely, is our natural state. Very young children often live with their hearts wide open. But somewhere along the way, we get our feelings hurt, we find ourselves with a "broken heart," and we start to find ways to protect our heart. We build walls around our heart, brick by brick, hurt by hurt.

You can't see these walls. They are built in a part of our imagination we can't always access. Sometimes we don't even know we are building these walls.

What we are left with is a thick, strong wall around the light in our heart. It's like the wall to a secret garden. Our heart's garden continues to grow and bloom for a while, but by keeping the hurt out of our heart, we are also keeping out the love. And when nothing can get into the garden, we also keep our feelings and love trapped inside the garden.

When you are ready to open your heart, try this:

1. Take a couple of pillows and place the short ends against your tailbone and lay back onto the pillows. Support your head with more pillows if necessary. You should be in a gentle backbend. Bend your knees or extend your legs—whichever feels best. (If this is uncomfortable, simply lie flat on your back.)

2. Close your eyes.

3. Take ten deep breaths.

4. As you breathe, bring your attention to your heart. Imagine it as a garden. What is growing in your heart garden?

5. Walk around your heart garden in your imagination.

6. Notice if you have a wall around the garden.

7. What is your wall built of? Is it low or high?

8. Can you begin to bring your wall down? Brick by brick? If it is a strong wall, you might have to envision a tool to help you. Remember, you built it; you can choose to bring it down. It might be as simple as asking the wall to dissolve. You might be able to blow the wall away into dust with the power of your breath. Be creative.

9. As you dissolve the wall around your heart, watch what happens to your garden. Imagine the vines and flowers growing with a burst of loving energy from the center of your heart out to fill your entire body. Your garden brings joy and love to every corner of your physical being.

10. Let it reach outside of you, growing to fill the room, to fill your town, to fill the world.

SITTING WITH HEARTBEATS · · · · · · · · ·

1. Find a comfortable seat.

2. Close your eyes.

3. You might want to put a hand or both over your heart.

4. Feel your heart beating in your chest.

5. Deepen your breath and feel your chest rise and fall as your breath circulates around your beating heart.

6. Is your heartbeat steady? Does it change? Do you think your heart knows you are holding it right now? Does it know you are listening?

7. *Are* you listening?

8. Is there more to hear or feel than the beating of your heart?

9. Once you tune in to your heart, you can talk to it. You and your heart are old friends. You've been together your entire life. Think of all you've been through together.

10. Thank your heart for being your steady and constant companion. You can depend on your heart.

11. Listen for your heart's reply. Chances are it is thanking you too for living the life that you do, for sharing your experiences with it. Even when you aren't intending to, you give your heart the rich experience of living a human life. Your heart's reply might happen in your imagination or with a shift in its pace.

12. Listen, feel, and give thanks.

DANCING TO THE BEAT OF YOUR HEART · · · · · · · · · · · · · ·

Time to dance . . .

1. Put on your favorite song.

2. Let the music work its way through your body.

3. Imagine that the beat of the song is the beating of your heart.

4. Dance like you are the music.

5. Close your eyes and let yourself go. Don't worry if your moves "match" the sound of the music. Maybe you really *are* dancing to the beat of your own heart. Just dance in a way that feels good. It doesn't matter how it looks. It matters how it feels.

6. Dance like no one is watching.

7. Dance to the song on repeat or create different dance mixes to match your moods. Create a mix for joy, sadness, frustration, anger, confusion, etc.

DANCE YOUR EMOTIONS.

DANCE ALONE.

DANCE WITH YOUR FAMILY.

JUST DANCE.

Use Easy Pose for meditation or to focus on your breathing.

You can use a wall or a tree to support your back. If it hurts your knees to sit cross-legged, use a pillow or folded towel to lift up your bum a little and stretch your legs out in front of you, bending the knees as much as you need to for your lower back.

1. Sit and breathe deeply into your lungs.

2. See if you can focus on filling the backside of your body with your breath, filling from the shoulder blades down your back body.

3. Relax and let go, using the support of the wall or tree behind you if necessary.

4. Use the fullness of your breath and the stillness of your body to relax and nourish your heart.

1. Lay on your back with your legs a little wider than your hips and your arms out along your sides, with palms facing up.

2. Relax every muscle in your body.

3. Let the earth beneath your body fully support you.

   If lying flat hurts your neck, roll up a towel and put it under the base of your head to take the strain off your neck. You can also place a rolled-up towel under your knees to help relax your lower back.

4. Let the ground hold you up now and rest—really rest.

   This is actually harder to do than you might think.

5. Imagine you are like a glass of water being spilled over a tabletop, with all the liquid in you spreading out to your outer edges.

   Close your eyes. With each breath see if you can release into a softer place. Once you feel more settled into the relaxation of the pose, with your mind's eye imagine your heart like a projector shining so brightly you light up the entire sky like the sun.

6. With each breath see if you can release into a softer place.

1. With a parent, a friend, or with yourself, sit for a moment and wonder about all that you are thankful for in your life.

2. Write down everything that comes to mind.

3. Do not stop until you run out of things to write down. No matter what bad or hard thing is going on in our lives, we all have many things to be grateful for:

> The light from the sun
>
> The magic of a rainbow
>
> A hug from someone who cares about us
>
> Chocolate
>
> Clean water

It feels so good to sit and honor the things that bring your heart joy. To bask in the glow of loving all the beautiful and brilliant things in your world, in your family, in your heart—is the greatest way to help your love grow.

Gratitude is not just something we feel. It is something we should actively practice, just like yoga poses. The act of sitting still and concentrating on all that we are thankful for shifts you into a state of joy.

Focusing on gratitude helps us to expand and radiate in every direction, like the sun.

Write or draw on the sunburst gratitude mandala.

NAMASTE (which means I bow to you)

From our shining hearts to yours, thank you for making the light in our hearts shine brighter by experimenting with us on this journey to reawaken your sensational body.

Slow down, tune in, and shine on with your beautiful selves!

This is meant to be a launching pad for your own brilliant ideas to journey, to know, and to listen to your heart. You know yourselves better than anyone else.

Love,

Laura and Whitney

WITH GRATITUDE ·

As we created this book, we realized we were writing a manual on how we'd like to live our lives—in gratitude with love and laughter and deeply connected to our sensational bodies. We were fortunate to work in collaboration with many friends who share those same values and who inspired us along our sensational journey.

We would like to offer a hearty thanks to our many teachers. To Mary-Lynn Masi, our Heartfulness meditation teacher, for keeping us in touch with our hearts. To Jacque Despardeau and Milly Stocker, our Chinese Medicine doctors for sharing your wisdom. To Suzy Meszoly for helping us navigate the world of quantum healing and beyond. To Barry Walker for helping us learn how to access the present moment. To Laura Lee for helping us to see the importance of this project. Thank you all for your encouragement and for sharing your unique perspectives with us.

We owe a great debt to the many talented artists, writers, and editors who helped us to shape this book. Laura Beers, your design genius, humor, and wisdom were invaluable. Lisa Zuniga and Dave Foxall, you looked beyond the horrible grammar of early drafts to help make a work of art. Adrian Pagdin, without your guidance this book would still exist only on our computers. Marc Tedeschi, your guidance came at a pivotal time and really set things into motion.

Danielle Coleman, your photography is stunning and we are so honored to work with you. Marianna Chavez, thank you for those early photos on very cold days. You showed us where this book could go and believed in us. To our models, Lily, Courtney, Shay, Bash, Riggs, Anna, and Leila—thank you for your patience and for your smiles. Thank you to Lara Stewart for incredible eleventh hour photographs. A hearty thanks to the wonderful Heike Coffee, our technology guru and web designer, and to images of Old Greenwich for your photo editing prowess.

Our early readers helped us steer the project and keep us from getting too "out there." Thank you to Kerri Maher, Cheryl Floyd, Kolleen Evers, Tracy Bechtel, and Nina Lindia.

We would also like to thank our community, Old Greenwich, CT. The support and enthusiasm we have received from our friends in OG has been the push we needed to keep going on this project. We originally began this manual as a toolkit for the teachers at Old Greenwich School. It's evolved into something bigger than we imagined, and we hope it will still make a difference at our hometown school.

Last, but not least, we would like to give a very special thank you to our families. You have always believed in us. Keep believing, because we are just getting started.

Love,
Whitney and Laura

NOTES